At the back of this book:

Updated Indiana Academic Standards for Reading, Writing, Listening, and Speaking!

Reading STREET

Indiana

Program Authors

Peter Afflerbach

Camille Blachowicz

Candy Dawson Boyd

Wendy Cheyney

Connie Juel

Edward Kame'enui

Donald Leu

Jeanne Paratore

P. David Pearson

Sam Sebesta

Deborah Simmons

Sharon Vaughn

Susan Watts-Taffe

Karen Kring Wixson

PEARSON

Scott Foresman

Editorial Offices: Glenview, Illinois • Parsippany, New Jersey • New York, New York
Sales Offices: Boston, Massachusetts • Duluth, Georgia • Glenview, Illinois
Coppell, Texas • Sacramento, California • Mesa, Arizona

We dedicate Reading Street to
Peter Jovanovich.

His wisdom, courage,
and passion for education
are an inspiration to us all.

About the Cover Artist

Daniel Moreton lives in New York City, where he uses his computer to create illustrations for books. When he is not working, Daniel enjoys cooking, watching movies, and traveling. On a trip to Mexico, Daniel was inspired by all of the bright colors around him. He likes to use those colors in his art.

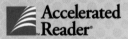

ISBN: 0-328-26104-1

Dear Indiana Reader,

Are you enjoying your travels along *Scott Foresman Reading Street?* What new skills have you learned to help you read and understand new things? What strategies have helped you smooth out the "bumps in the road" as you read?

As you continue along *Scott Foresman Reading Street,* you will read about people in communities at home, in school, and in neighborhoods. You will also read about communities in nature. So, buckle your seat belt and enjoy the trip!

Sincerely,
The Authors

What is a community?

People in Communities

Communities in Nature

Communities

What is a community?

Let's Talk About People in Communities

Words to Read

want
good
catch
no
put

Read the Words

1. Max said, "I want a fish."

2. Fish are good to eat.

3. Will Max catch a fish?

4. No fish bit.

5. We put the fish in a pan.

Max and Ruby

A Big Fish for Max

Genre: Animal Fantasy
An animal fantasy is a story with animals that act like humans. Next you will read about Max and Ruby—rabbits that go fishing.

Max and Ruby

A Big Fish for Max

written and designed by

Rosemary Wells

illustrated

by Jody Wheeler

Where will Max get a big fish?

"I wish I had a fish to eat," said Max.

"Then we will catch a big fish,"
said Grandma.

"We can walk to the park," said Ruby.

"And Max will catch a big fish."

"Good," said Max. "Yum, yum, yum!"

The path in the park led to the pond.

"Max can fish in this pond," said Ruby.

Max sat.

He got a red ball in his net.

But no fish bit.

Then Max got a black ship in his net.
But no fish bit.

And then Max got a clam shell
in his net.

"I want to call the fish," said Ruby.
"Then I can talk to the fish."
But still no fish bit.

"Well, we can all walk to the fish shop," said Grandma.
"And we can talk to the fish man."

The fish man had lots of fish in a box.
"We want a fresh fish," said Grandma.
"That fat fish is good."

At home, Grandma put the fish
in a hot pan.
Then Ruby put the fish in a dish.

"Yum, yum, yum!" said Max.

Think and Share

Talk About It Max, Ruby, and Grandma care about each other. Find and read one part of the story that shows caring.

1. Use the pictures below to retell the story.

2. What was this story mostly about?

3. As you read, did you predict that Max would catch a fish? Find the part of the story that shows whether you were right.

Look Back and Write Look back at pages 20–22. Max did not catch a fish. What did he catch? Write those things.

Rosemary Wells

Ms. Wells says, "Some of my most pleasurable memories as a child were of fishing with my father. We used to catch snapper blues, and my mother cooked them in parsley and butter that night. Today fish is still one of my favorite things to eat."

When Rosemary Wells writes stories about Max and Ruby, she thinks about what her own two girls said and did when they were children.

Read other books by Rosemary Wells.

At Home

We all want to help.
This plant is no good.
We dig it up.

Dad puts pots on the shelf.

Mom cuts the grass.

Sis can catch Gus.
We talk and have fun.

Nouns

· ·

A **noun** names a person, a place, an animal, or a thing.

· ·

The word **man** names a person.

The word **park** names a place.

The word **fish** names an animal.

The word **net** names a thing.

Write Using Nouns

1. Write the three things Max got in his net. Their names are nouns.

· ·

2. What place did Max, Ruby, and Grandma visit? Write a sentence about it. Draw a line under each noun.

· ·

3. What did Max do to get a fish? Write the steps he took. Draw a line under each noun you use.

Let's Talk About

People in Communities

Words to Read

| could |
| be |
| old |
| paper |
| horse |

Read the Words

1. Dave could be the pig in the class play.

2. Beth has an old hat for the play.

3. The class made paper masks.

4. Jake made a horse mask.

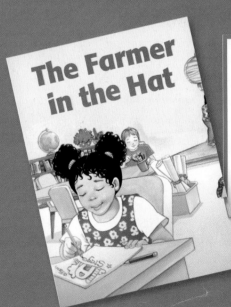

Genre: Realistic Fiction
Realistic fiction has characters that act like real people. You will read a story about classmates putting on a play.

The Farmer in the Hat

by Pat Cummings

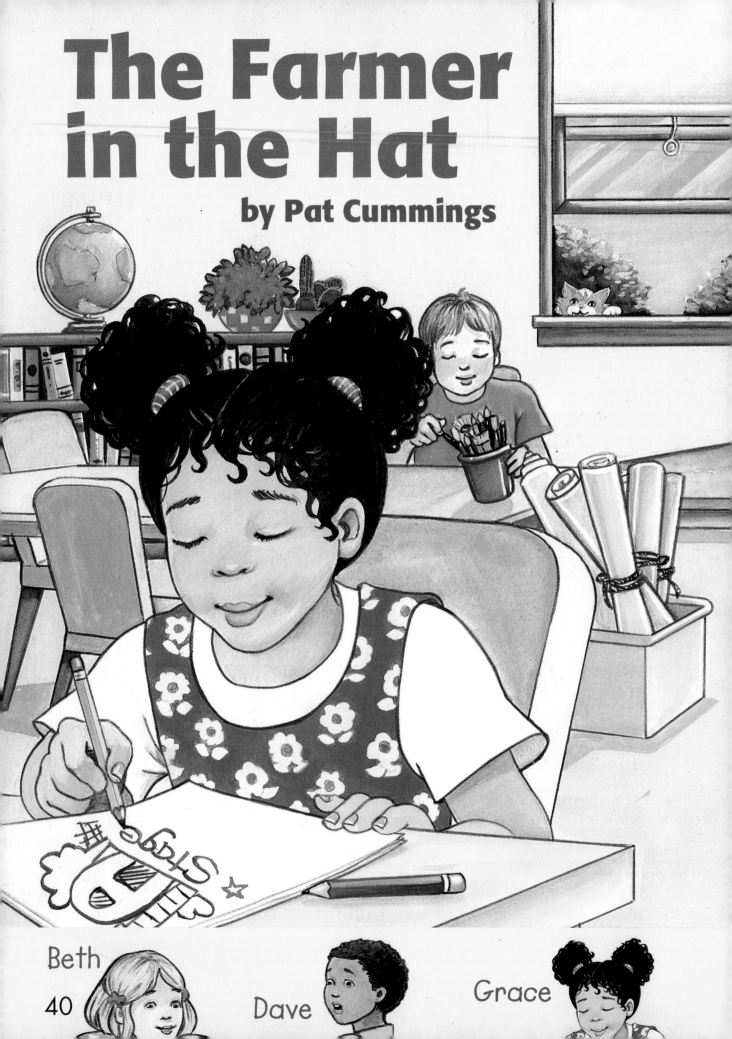

Beth

Dave

Grace

Who will be the farmer in the play?

Max

Jake

Meg

41

"I have the hat. I could be the farmer, Old MacDonald, in this play," said Beth.

"No, I will be the
farmer," said Dave.

"You can be a pig," said Beth.
"A pig!" Dave made a face.

Grace went up on the stage. "We could make paper masks," she said. "Ducks, hens, a pig, a horse!"

"I have the hat!" said Max.
"I will be Old MacDonald,
not Beth!"

"Let me have that hat!" Dave said.

"Stop!" said Grace. "We must make masks."

Old MacDonald
★ Hens = Beth and Grace
★ Pig = Dave
★ Duck = Max
★ Farmer = ?

Max made a duck on his page.
Beth made hens.

Dave made a pig mask on his page.

"That is one odd pig," Grace said.

"It takes ages to make this horse mask," said Jake.

"I can make my mask fast," said Meg.

She made a fat gerbil mask.

"Place that gerbil in a paper cage,"
Jake said with a grin.

"Take your places up on the stage," said Grace.

"Grunt!" Dave had on his pig mask.

"Squeak!" said Meg.

"Quack!" Max had on his duck mask.

"Cluck." Beth had on her hen mask.

"Look at the cat!" said Grace.
"That is one odd farmer!"

Think and Share

Talk About It The author wrote a funny story about a class play. Read your favorite part of the story.

1. Use the pictures below to retell the story.

2. Why did the children forget about the farmer's hat?

3. The pictures give a clue about how the story will end. What clues do you see?

Look Back and Write Look back at the story. List the animals that will be in the play.

Meet the Author and Illustrator

Pat Cummings

Pat Cummings once played a rabbit in a school play, and her sister played a grasshopper. Ms. Cummings made the cat the farmer in this story because "cats seem to naturally find the center of attention."

Ms. Cummings loves writing children's books. "The best part is that I can explore almost any subject."

Read two more books by Pat Cummings.

Helping Hands at 4-H

by Lindy Russell

Where could you see what farmers do? At a 4-H club!

How old are kids in 4-H? They can be ages 8 to 18.

At 4-H you can take care of
a horse or a pig.

You can get the eggs from the hens.

This 4-H club has a bake sale.
They place an ad in the paper.
They sell eggs too.

The sale is good!
The club will get chicks.

The chicks will get big.
Then the club will have lots
of eggs to sell.

Proper Nouns

· ·

Special names for people, places, animals, and things are called **proper nouns.** Proper nouns begin with capital letters.

· ·

Max took the hat from **B**eth.

Max and **B**eth are proper nouns. They tell the names of a girl and a boy. **M**ax and **B**eth begin with capital letters.

Write Using Proper Nouns

1. Pick three children from the story. Their names are proper nouns. Write their names.

. . . .

2. Your name and your friend's name are proper nouns. Write a sentence using your name and a friend's name. Did you use capital letters?

. . . .

3. Could you make a mask for Old MacDonald? How would you do it? Write the steps. Use capital letters for proper nouns.

Let's Talk About
People in
Communities

Mayor Sterling

65

Words to Read

| people |
| live |
| work |
| who |
| out |

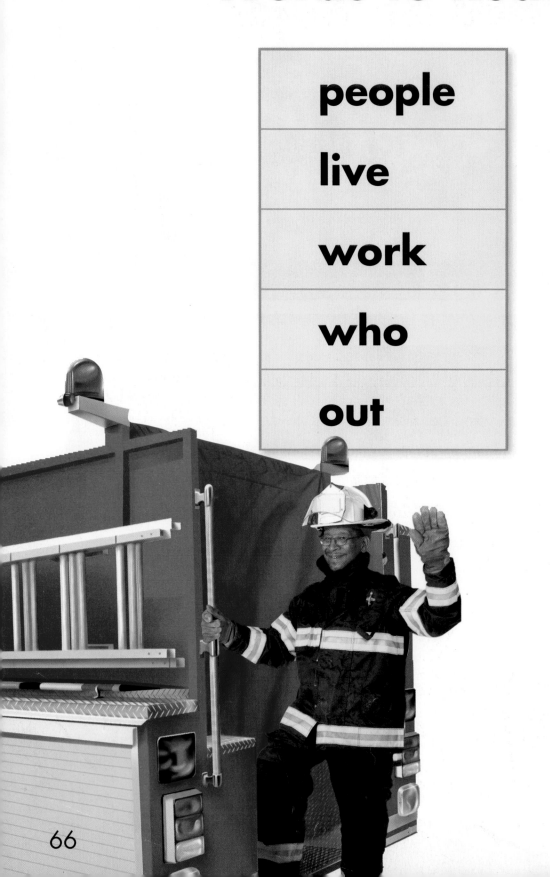

Read the Words

1. People live here.

2. People work here too.

3. Who works here?

4. Who puts out fires?

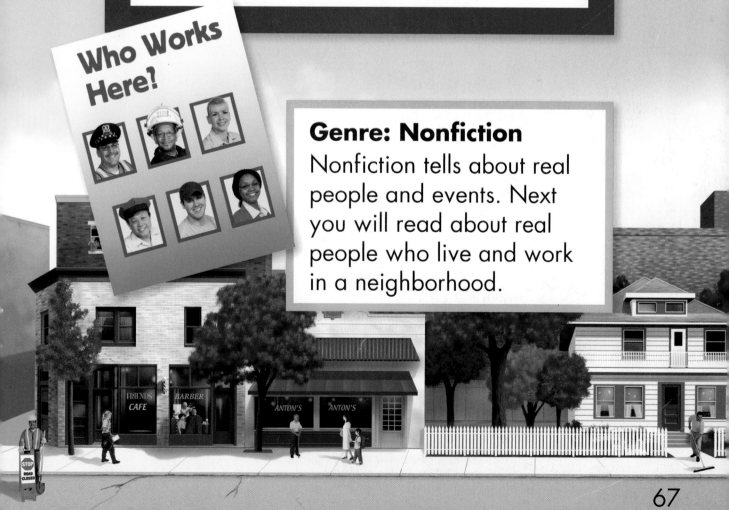

Who Works Here?

Genre: Nonfiction
Nonfiction tells about real people and events. Next you will read about real people who live and work in a neighborhood.

Who Works

Who works where you live?

Here?

by Melissa Blackwell Burke

illustrated by Tim Spransy

People live and work
in this neighborhood.
It is such a busy place.

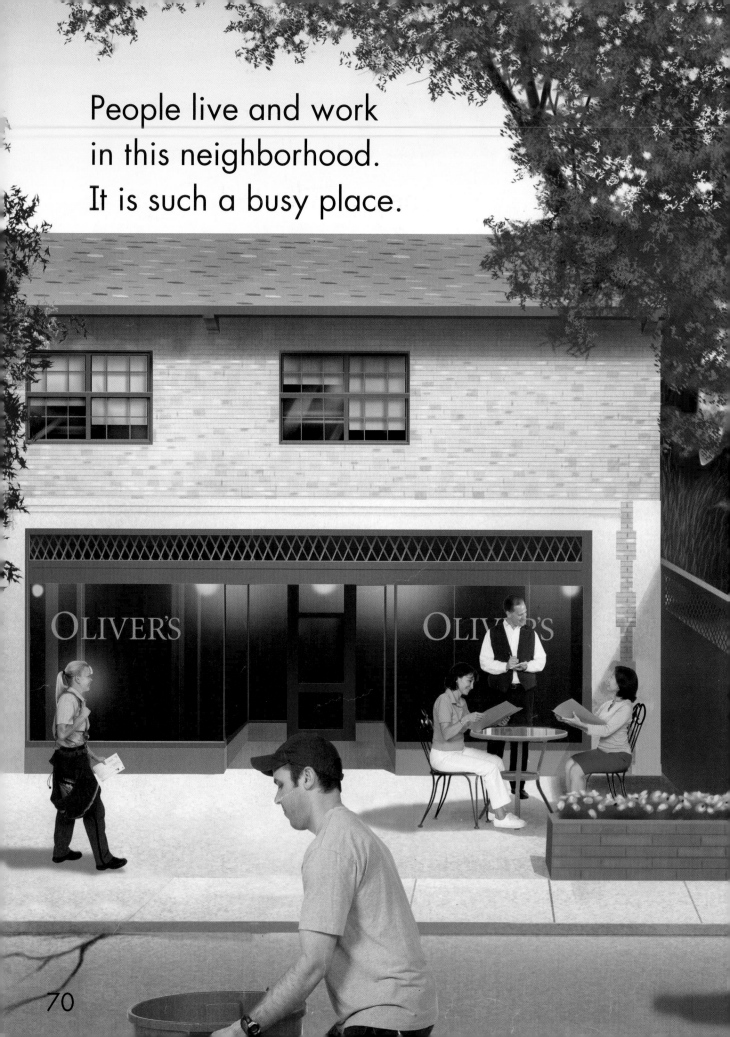

Who works in this place?
We will talk to them.
They all like to help us.

I make the neighborhood safe.
When you ride your bike,
stop and check all ways.
I will help you cross.

I help put out fires. Fire can be bad.
I wish all people could be safe
from fire.

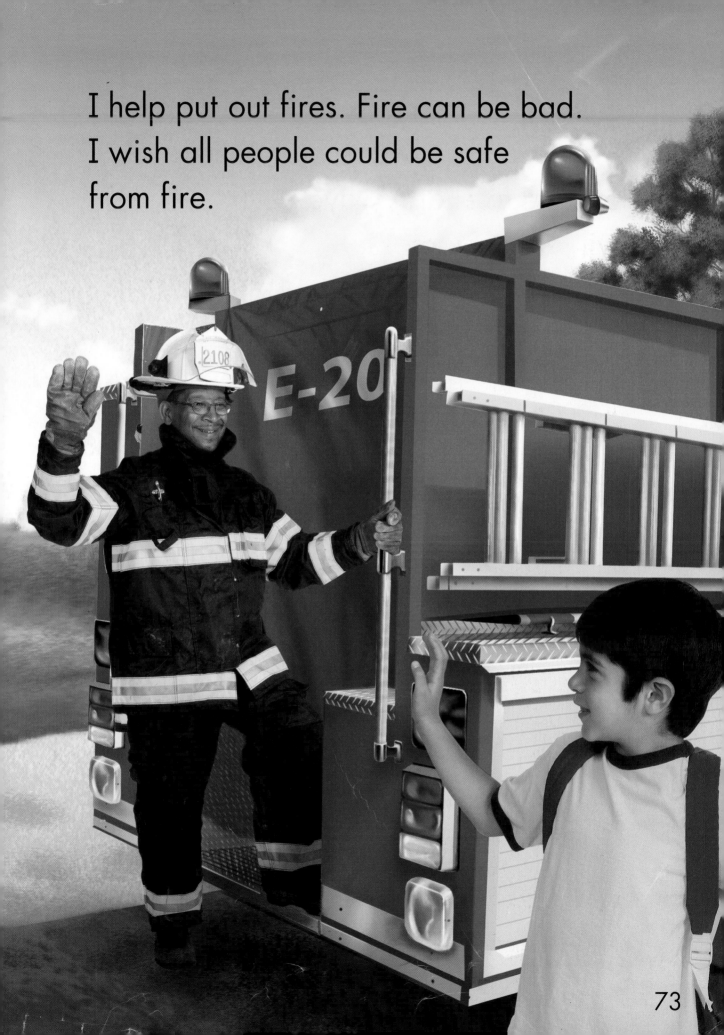

I put mail in your box.
People stop and wave and smile.
They like to chat a while.

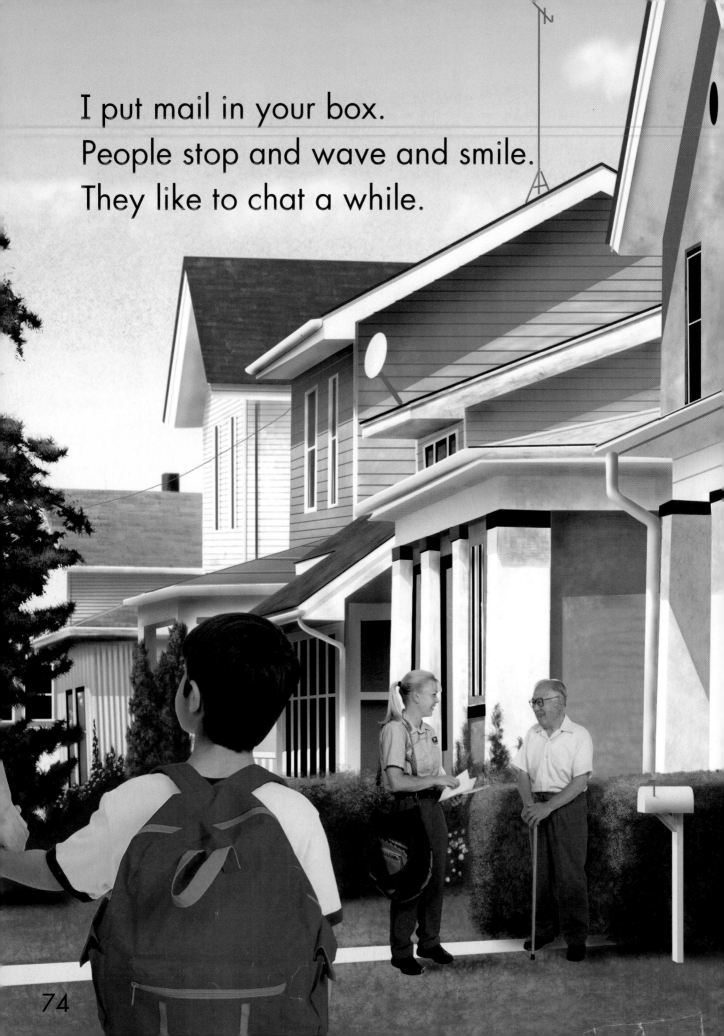

I drive a big bus.
People can ride this bus to work.
I stop and pick them up.

I pick up trash.
When people put it out,
I pitch it in this truck.

Who works where you live?
Smile at them.
You will like them!

Think and Share

Talk About It *Who Works Here?* is about workers in a community. Tell about the job that interests you the most.

1. Use the pictures below to summarize what you learned.

2. What important information did the author want you to know?

3. Did anything confuse you? What question did you ask yourself as you read?

Look Back and Write Look back at page 77. What does this worker do?

Meet the Author

Melissa Blackwell Burke

Melissa Blackwell Burke grew up in a small town in Texas. She loved to visit the library. She says, "When I was a little girl, I wanted to be many things, including a teacher, a newspaper reporter, and a librarian. I have been two of those—a teacher and a newspaper reporter. Who knows—I might still become a librarian some day!"

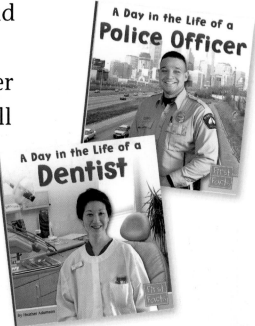

Read other books about neighborhood workers.

Neighborhood Map

Use this map to check out where people live and work in this busy neighborhood.

- Who works on Pine Lane?

- Who works on Park Drive?

- Where is the bus stop?

- Where can you get stamps?

- Where is the truck that picks up the trash?

White Lane

Elm Drive

Park Drive

Pine Lane

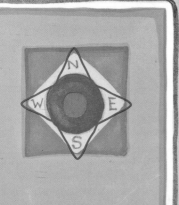

Read Together

Special Titles

A **title** can come before the name of a person. A title begins with a capital letter. Some titles end with a **period(.)**.

Officer Black helps me cross the street.

Ms. Timms brings us letters.

Dr. Vann is a vet.

Officer, Ms., and **Dr.** are special titles. Each begins with a capital letter. The titles **Ms.** and **Dr.** end with periods.

Write Using Special Titles

1. Make up names for some of the workers in *Who Works Here?* Write their names using special titles with capital letters and periods.

2. Write a sentence about someone who works in your neighborhood. Use capital letters and periods for special titles.

3. How does your teacher start your school day? Write about it. Use capital letters and periods for special titles.

Let's Talk About Communities in Nature

Words to Read

there

down

inside

now

together

Read the Words

1. I smell a baby there.

2. T. Rex ran up the slope and down.

3. The small animals went inside the circle.

4. Now T. Rex couldn't get his lunch.

5. They like being together.

The Big Circle

Genre: Fiction

Fiction stories are made-up stories. Next you will read a made-up story about dinosaurs that lived a long time ago.

The Big Circle

by Eric Kimmel

illustrated by Richard Bernal

Who lived here long ago?

Big T. Rex wakes up.
Now Big T. Rex wants to eat,
but not bones and not stones.

Big T. Rex wants meat to eat.

Here is a herd of triceratops.
They are going home.

There they can get good grass
to munch. The grass at home
will make them fat.

Sniff, sniff. "Hmm," said Big T. Rex. "My nose smells a baby there. I'm good at hunting. I'll get that baby. It will make a good lunch."

Big T. Rex rose up on his back legs. He ran up the slope and down. The herd saw T. Rex run up and down.

They had time to make a big circle. The small animals went inside the circle. The baby went inside too.

Big T. Rex didn't like this.
Now he couldn't get his lunch.

But T. Rex didn't quit. "I'll make that herd run," he said.

But the herd didn't run.
They kept still in the big circle.

Then they gave T. Rex a poke and a bump. Together they drove him back.

Big T. Rex ran back up the slope and down. Those triceratops saw T. Rex run. Now they are safe.

They are going home to munch grass. Big T. Rex can't get them now. They like being together.

Think and Share

Talk About It The author wrote an exciting story about dinosaurs. Which part of the story did you like best? Why?

1. Use the pictures below to retell the story.

2. What happened after the triceratops saw Big T. Rex?

3. As you read the story, did anything confuse you? What did you do?

Test Practice

Look Back and Write Look back at the selection. Write about how the triceratops protect the baby.

Meet the Author and the Illustrator

Eric Kimmel

As a boy Eric Kimmel visited the Museum of Natural History in New York City almost every weekend. "The dinosaur skeletons were old friends," he says. "Triceratops and stegosaurus were my favorites."

Richard Bernal

Richard Bernal drew the pictures for this story. "I love dinosaurs," he says. "I have several dinosaur toys in my studio."

Read other books by Eric Kimmel and Richard Bernal.

Class Paper

Ms. Bell and Class Take Trip

Big Bones

Ms. Bell and her class went on a trip. They saw bones from a T. Rex.

They saw bones from
a triceratops. There aren't
animals like this now.

Cave Men

The class sat down and saw a film telling of cave men. Cave men went inside caves to live. They went hunting together.

Ms. Bell said, "I'm glad we went on this trip. We'll take many trips like this."

Days, Months, and Holidays

Days of the week, **months** of the year, and **holidays** all begin with capital letters.

Big T. Rex woke up on **Saturday.**

The triceratops went home to munch grass in **March.**

Mother's Day is next **Sunday.**

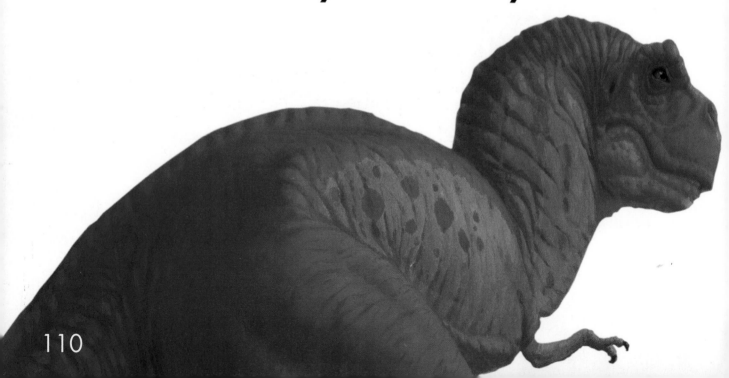

Write Using Days, Months, and Holidays

1. When is your birthday? Write the month. Look at a calendar. On what day of the week is your birthday this year? Write the day. Use capital letters.

· ·

2. Write a sentence about your favorite month. Be sure to use capital letters correctly.

· ·

3. What if there were a Dinosaur's Day? Tell two things you could do to celebrate this holiday.

Let's Talk About Communities in Nature

Words to Read

grow
food
around
find
water
under

Read the Words

1. The sun helps plants and trees grow.

2. Plants are good food for insects.

3. Birds look around to find insects to eat.

4. Water makes logs damp.

5. Grubs live under rocks and logs.

Life in the Forest

Genre: Expository Nonfiction
Expository nonfiction tells facts about real places. Next you will read about the plants and animals in a forest.

Life in the Forest

by Claire Daniel

What lives in the forest?

We can find life all around the forest.
It is a busy place!

The sun helped these leaves grow wide and flat.

Sun shines on the leaves
and helps them grow.
Many bugs like eating leaves.
Yum, yum! The bugs eat and eat.

A woodpecker sits on a branch.
Peck! Peck! Peck!
The woodpecker pecks for bugs.

These holes tell us that a woodpecker has pecked on this tree.

This huge log is soft and damp.
Water has made the log rot.
Small bugs made a home in the log.

This bird hops on the log
and pecks at it. Yum, yum!
It gets bugs from the log.

Nuts grow on trees and then
fall all around. Squirrels find
the nuts and eat them.

124

A fox is cute, but it likes to catch small animals like squirrels.

The black bear eats leaves, grass, and nuts. It likes grubs too. Grubs are small bugs under rocks and logs.

This bear looked for grubs under these rocks.

A hummingbird uses its bill to get food from this plant.

Many plants have shapes like tubes. Small hummingbirds like to sip food and water from these plants.

Hummingbirds can catch bugs
for food too.

The forest is filled with life.
Many animals and plants call it home.
It is a busy place!

Think and Share

Talk About It Tell what you learned about the forest that you didn't know before.

1. Use the pictures below to summarize what you learned about life in the forest.

2. Why do you think the author wrote *Life in the Forest?*

3. What did you do to get ready to read *Life in the Forest?* How did that help you?

Test Practice

Look Back and Write Look back at pages 124–125. What do the squirrel and the fox eat?

Claire Daniel

Claire Daniel learned about forests on a three-month hiking trip with her husband. "That was an amazing experience—being in the forest and living in it."

A bear came to their campsite once. "We heard him coming, so we ran to a shelter. It was a frightening experience! The bear went into our tent and then backed out of it, not finding any food."

Read more books by Claire Daniel.

A Mangrove

Have you watched fish
swim under a tree?
You can find fish in this forest.
These trees grow in salt water.
Fish swim under the trees.

Forest

by Terry Lynk
illustrated by Russell Farrell

Lots of animals live here.

Some live in the water.

Some live out of the water.

They are all around this forest.

Fish find food in the water.
Birds can use fish
and bugs as food.

But some forests like this
are being lost. We must
save these forests.

One and More Than One

Many nouns add **-s** to mean more than one.

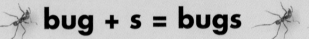 **nut + s = nuts**

bug + s = bugs

This bear looked for **grubs** under these **rocks.**

The bear is looking for more than one grub. It is looking under more than one rock.

Write Using One and More Than One

1. Pick three forest animals from *Life in the Forest.* Write the words that name them. Then write the words again to show more than one.

· ·

2. Write a sentence telling what squirrels eat. Use **-s** to show more than one.

· ·

3. How do woodpeckers get their food? Write about what they eat and how they get it. Use **-s** to show more than one.

Let's Talk About
Communities in Nature

Words to Read

family
other
also
their
some
new

Read the Words

1. The queen bee rules the bee family.

2. Other bees also live in the hive.

3. These bees do their jobs well.

4. Some bees will make a new hive.

Honey Bees

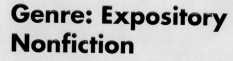

Genre: Expository Nonfiction

Expository nonfiction tells facts about real people, places, or animals. This article tells about honey bees.

Honey Bees

by Jesús Cervantes

illustrated by Tom Leonard

What happens
inside a bee hive?

The sun shines. The honey bees wake up. It is time for these insects to work.

Buzz,
buzz,
buzz.

In the hive, bees live together
like a family. In the family, there
is a queen bee, many worker
bees, and some drones.

This is the <u>queen</u> bee.
She rules the hive.

These are the drones.
They help the <u>queen</u>.

Their hive is hidden in a tree.
Worker bees keep this hive safe.

It is not good to make bees mad!
Bees will attack.

Worker bees make wax cells in the hive. These wax cells are small holes.

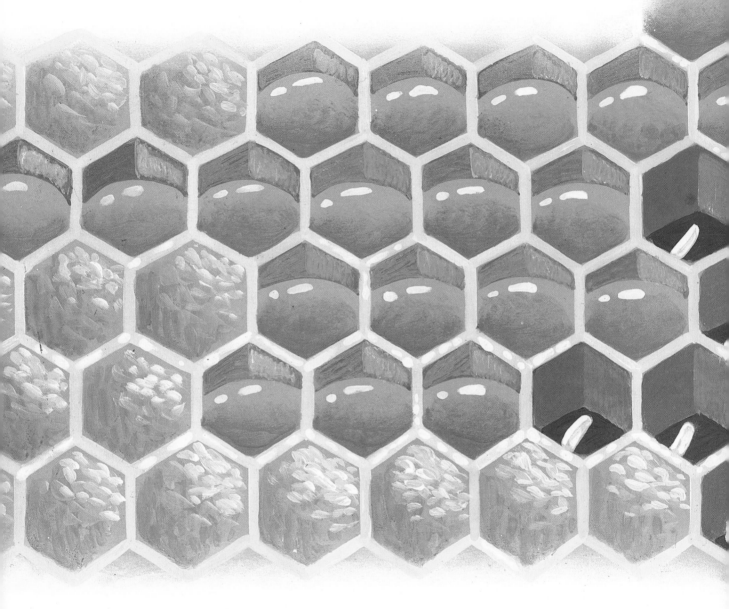

Bees save honey in some wax cells. Little bees live and grow in other cells.

Honey is food for bees. Worker bees feed honey to other bees in the hive. Bees make honey from nectar.

Bees get nectar from flowers.
Honey bees find flowers with sweet
nectar. They take this sweet nectar
back inside their hive.

Worker bees also get
pollen from flowers.

Worker bees feed pollen to
the queen bee and the little bees.
It helps them grow big.

When those little bees get big,
it is time for a new hive.

Worker bees make the new hive.
A new queen will also go with them.

When it gets cold, the bees
will go inside their hive to
sleep and rest. The bees will
wake up when the sun shines.

Think and Share

Talk About It Worker bees are very busy. What do you think is their most important job? Read the part that tells about it.

1. Use the pictures below to tell what you learned about honey bees.

2. How are a queen bee and a worker bee alike? How are they different?

3. What question did you have about bees before reading? How did that help you?

Look Back and Write What kinds of bees live in a hive? Look back at page 146.

Jesús Cervantes

Jesús Cervantes grew up on a lemon and avocado ranch in southern California. He says, "The ranch had lots of bees. They were brought in to pollinate the trees. I wasn't afraid of bees when I was growing up."

Mr. Cervantes thinks bees are great. He says, "I love honey when it's still on the comb."

Read more about bees.

The Ants Go Marching

The ants go marching one by one,
Hurrah, hurrah.
The ants go marching one by one,
Hurrah, hurrah.
The ants go marching one by one,
The little one stops to have some fun.

And they all go marching down,
To the ground,
To get out
Of the rain.
BOOM! BOOM! BOOM! BOOM!

illustrated by Norman Gorbaty

Nouns in Sentences

A **noun** names a person, place, animal, or thing. A noun can be in more than one place in a sentence.

Their **hive** is hidden in a **tree.**

Both **hive** and **tree** are nouns. **Hive** is in the naming part of the sentence. **Tree** is in the action part of the sentence.

Write Using Nouns in Sentences

1. Write this sentence. Circle all of the nouns.

The bees will feed the queen.

· ·

2. Write a sentence that tells what bees get from flowers. Circle the nouns in your sentence.

· ·

3. How does the queen bee get her food? Write about it. Circle the nouns you use.

Thanks for the Help

connect to **WRITING**

In this unit, you read about many different communities. Think of people in your community who help you every day. Write a thank-you letter to one of these people. Draw a picture of this person.

Dear Mail Carrier,
Thank you for bringing me letters.
You do a good job.

Your pal,
Matt

Flower Power

connect to
SCIENCE

The hummingbirds in *Life in the Forest* and the bees in *Honey Bees* both need flowers. Draw a picture that shows how bees and hummingbirds use flowers. Then write a caption that tells about your picture.

Make a Chart

connect to
MATH

You have read six stories about communities. Which did you like best? Which did your classmates like? Take a vote. Make a chart with the story titles. Mark a line to show each vote. Give the story with the most votes a star.

Stories	Votes
A Big Fish for Max	|||
The Farmer in the Hat	|||
Who Works Here?	||
⭐ The Big Circle	||||
Life in the Forest	||
Honey Bees	|||

Pictionary

My Family

mom
mama
mother
mommy

sister
daughter

dad
papa
father
daddy

This is me!

These are my relatives.

son
brother

uncle   cousin   aunt

baby

grandma
grandmother

grandpa
grandfather

Pictionary

My School

chalkboard

map

chalk

teacher

books

computer

ruler

eraser

pencil

scissors

clock

bulletin board

school

flag

playground

student

crayon

cafeteria

table

chair

classroom

lunchbox

Pictionary

Where People Live

houseboat

pueblo

log cabin

mobile home

high-rise

house

apartment building

townhouse

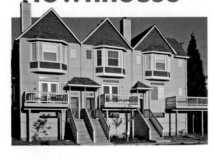

Pictionary

Where Animals Live

anthill

nest

hive

cave

den

log

barn

burrow

ocean

lodge

Pictionary

My Town

school

grocery store

bus driver

post office

crossing guard

mail carrier

garbage collector

barber shop

library

barber

librarian

cashier

bus stop

fire truck

firefighter

police officer

park

gardener

173

Tested Words

Max and Ruby:
A Big Fish for Max

catch
good
no
put
want

The Farmer in
the Hat

be
could
horse
old
paper

Who Works Here?

live
out
people
who
work

The Big Circle

down
inside
now
there
together

Life in the Forest

around
find
food
grow
under
water

Honey Bees

also
family
new
other
some
their

Acknowledgments

Illustrations

Cover: Daniel Moreton

8, 164 Mark Buehner

11-35 Jody Wheeler

38 Pat Cummings

68-77 Tim Spransy

74-75 April Mosakowski Hartmann

78-102 Richard Bernal

132-135 Russell Farrell

138 Amy Vangsgard

142-157 Tom Leonard

144 Norman Gorbaty

172 Stephen Lewis

Photographs

Every effort has been made to secure permission and provide appropriate credit for photographic material. The publisher deeply regrets any omission and pledges to correct errors called to its attention in subsequent editions.

Unless otherwise acknowledged, all photographs are the property of Scott Foresman, a division of Pearson Education.

Photo locators denoted as follows: Top (T), Center (C), Bottom (B), Left (L), Right (R), Background (Bkgd).

9 ©Bill Ross/Corbis

10 ©Gabe Palmer/Corbis

11 (T) ©Tom & Dee Ann McCarthy/Corbis, (BL) ©Sean Justice/Getty Images, (CR) ©Britt Erlanson/Getty Images

36 ©Ariel Skelley/Corbis

37 (TL) ©LWA-Dann Tardif/Corbis, (BL) ©Tom & Dee Ann McCarthy/Corbis, (TR) ©Gabe Palmer/Corbis

57, 58 Wagner Farm, Glenview Park District, Glenview, IL.

60 (CR, CL) ©G K & Vikki Hart/Getty Images

61 ©Melanie Acevedo/FoodPix

64 Getty Images

65 (T) ©Patrick Ward/Corbis, (BL) ©Michael Newman/PhotoEdit

84 ©Stephen Wilkes/Getty Images

85 (T) ©Paul Souders/Getty Images, (BL) ©Stephen Frink/Corbis

113 ©Royalty-Free/Corbis

114 ©Naturfoto Honal/Corbis

115 ©Steve Kaufman/Corbis

116 ©Bill Ross/Corbis

117 (TR) Photowood Inc./Corbis, (TL) Steve Kaufman/Corbis, (CL, BR) ©Royalty-Free/Corbis

118 (C) ©Photowood Inc./Corbis, (BL) ©Tom Uhlman/Visuals Unlimited

119 ©Steve Kaufman/Corbis

120 ©Naturfoto Honal/Corbis

121 ©Fritz Polking/Visuals Unlimited

122 ©Jamie Harron/Papilio/Corbis

124 ©Stephen Dalton/Photo Researchers, Inc.

125 (TR) ©Gerard Fuehrer/Visuals Unlimited, (B) Getty Images

126 (T) ©Jim Clare/Nature Picture Library

127 (T) ©Frederick D. Atwood

128 (Bkgd) ©Bill Ross/Corbis, (BR) ©Royalty-Free/Corbis, (TR) ©Melissa Farlow/Aurora & Quanta Productions, (CL) ©Gary W. Carter/Corbis, (TL) ©Bill Dyer/Photo Researchers, Inc.

129 (TL) ©Stephen Krasemann/Getty Images, (BR) ©Tim Thompson/Corbis

131 ©John Kreis Photography

135 ©Theo Allofs/Danita Delimont, Agent

136 Getty Images

137 ©Stephen Dalton/Photo Researchers, Inc.

138 (BC) ©Ewing Galloway/Index Stock Imagery, (CR) ©Tim Laman/NGS Image Collection

139 (TL) ©Karen Moskowitz/Getty Images, (CC) © Colombini Medeiros, Fabio/Animals Animals/Earth Scenes

168 ©Tim Ridley/DK Images

169 (CR) ©Richard Orton/Index Stock Imagery, (BCR) ©Mary Kate Denny/PhotoEdit, (TR) ©David R. Frazier/Photolibrary, Inc./Alamy Images, (BR) ©Ed Bock/Corbis

170 (TL) ©Jan Butchofsky-Houser/Corbis, (TR) ©E. R. Degginger/Color-Pic, Inc., (BCL) ©Royalty-Free/Corbis, (CC) ©Richard Bickel/Corbis, (BC) ©Kim Sayer/Corbis, (TCL) ©Tony Perrottet/Omni Photo Communications, (BL) Getty Images, (BR) ©John Coletti/DK Images

171 (BR) ©Steve Shott/DK Images, (BL) ©Douglas Peebles/Corbis, (TR) ©Karen Moskowitz/Getty Images, (BC) ©Roger Leo/Index Stock Imagery, (CC) ©Stouffer Productions/Animals Animals/Earth Scenes, (TC) ©Frank Greenaway/Courtesy of the National Prey Centre, Cloucestershire/DK Images, (BCL, TL, CL) Getty Images, (CR) ©Fritz Polking/Visuals Unlimited, (TR) ©Frank Greenaway/DK Images

Glossary

The contents of this glossary have been adapted from *First Dictionary*. Copyright ©2000, Pearson Education, Inc.

Indiana

Academic Standards

English/Language Arts

Grade 1

READING: Word Recognition, Fluency, and Vocabulary Development

Students understand the basic features of words. They see letter patterns and know how to translate them into spoken language by using phonics (an understanding of the different letters that make different sounds), syllables, and word parts (-s, -ed, -ing). They apply this knowledge to achieve fluent (smooth and clear) oral and silent reading.

Concepts About Print

1.1.1 Match oral words to printed words.

1.1.2 Identify letters, words, and sentences.

1.1.3 Recognize that sentences start with capital letters and end with punctuation, such as periods, question marks, and exclamation points.

Phonemic Awareness

1.1.4 Distinguish beginning, middle, and ending sounds in single-syllable words (words with only one vowel sound).
Example: Tell the sound that comes at the beginning of the word *sun*. Tell the sound that comes at the end of the word *cloud*. Tell the sound that comes in the middle of the word *boat*.

1.1.5 Recognize different vowel sounds in orally stated single-syllable words.
Example: Say the sound that is in the middle of the word *bit*. Say the sound that is in the middle of the word *bite*. Tell whether this is the same sound or a different sound.

1.1.6 Recognize that vowels' sounds can be represented by different letters.

1.1.7 Create and state a series of rhyming words.

1.1.8 Add, delete, or change sounds to change words.
Example: Tell what letter you would have to change to make the word *cow* into the word *how*. Tell what letter you would have to change to make the word *pan* into *an*.

1.1.9 Blend two to four phonemes (sounds) into recognizable words.
Example: Tell what word is made by the sounds /b/ /a/ /t/. Tell what word is made by the sounds /fl/ /a/ /t/.

Decoding and Word Recognition

1.1.10   Generate the sounds from all the letters and from a variety of letter patterns, including consonant blends and long- and short-vowel patterns (*a, e, i, o, u*), and blend those sounds into recognizable words.

1.1.19   Identify important signs and symbols, such as stop signs, school crossing signs, or restroom symbols, from the colors, shapes, logos, and letters on the signs or symbols.

1.1.11   Read common sight words (words that are often seen and heard).

1.1.12   Use phonic and context clues as self-correction strategies when reading.

1.1.13   Read words by using knowledge of vowel digraphs (two vowels that make one sound such as the *ea* in *eat*) and knowledge of how vowel sounds change when followed by the letter *r* (such as the *ea* in the word *ear*).
Example: Correctly read aloud the vowel sounds made in words, such as *ear, eat, near, their,* or *wear.*

1.1.14   Read common word patterns (*-ite, -ate*).
Example: Read words, such as *gate, late,* and *kite.*

1.1.15   Read aloud smoothly and easily in familiar text.

Vocabulary and Concept Development

1.1.16   Read and understand simple compound words (*birthday, anything*) and contractions (*isn't, aren't, can't, won't*).

1.1.17   Read and understand root words (*look*) and their inflectional forms (*looks, looked, looking*).
Example: Recognize that the *s* added to the end of *chair* makes it mean more than one chair. Recognize that adding *ed* to the end of *jump* makes it mean jumping that happened in the past.

1.1.18   Classify categories of words.
Example: Tell which of the following are fruits and which are vegetables: bananas, oranges, apples, carrots, and peas.

Standard 2

READING: Comprehension and Analysis of Nonfiction and Informational Text

Students read and understand grade-level-appropriate material. The selections in the **Indiana Reading List** *(www.doe.state.in.us/standards/readinglist.html) illustrate the quality and complexity of the materials to be read by students. At Grade 1, in addition to regular classroom reading, students begin to read a variety of nonfiction, such as alphabet books, picture books, books in different subject areas, children's magazines and periodicals, and beginners' dictionaries).*

Structural Features of Informational Materials

1.2.1   Identify the title, author, illustrator, and table of contents of a reading selection.

1.2.2   Identify text that uses sequence or other logical order.
Example: Explain how an informational text is different from a story. Tell what might be included in an informational book that uses sequence, such as a book on making a bird feeder like *The Bird Table* by Pauline Cartwright.

Analysis of Grade-Level-Appropriate Nonfiction and Informational Text

1.2.3   Respond to *who, what, when, where, why,* and *how* questions and recognize the main idea of what is read.
Example: After reading or listening to the science book *Gator or Croc* by Allan Fowler, students answer questions about the reptiles and discuss the main ideas.

1.2.4   Follow one-step written instructions.

1.2.5   Use context (the meaning of the surrounding text) to understand word and sentence meanings.

1.2.6   Draw conclusions or confirm predictions about what will happen next in a text by identifying key words (signal words that alert the reader to a sequence of events, such as *before, first, during, while, as, at the same time, after, then, next, at last, finally, now, when* or cause and effect, such as *because, since, therefore, so*).
Example: Read *Bats: Creatures of the Night* by Joyce Milton and discuss what words give clues about predicting where bats could be found or how they locate food.

1.2.7   Relate prior knowledge to what is read.
Example: Before reading *How Much Is a Million?* by David Schwartz, discuss students' estimates of large quantities.

Standard
3

READING: Comprehension and Analysis of Literary Text

Students read and respond to a wide variety of children's literature. The selections in the **Indiana Reading List** *(www.doe.state.in.us/standards/readinglist.html) illustrate the quality and complexity of the materials to be read by students. At Grade 1, students begin to read a wide variety of fiction, such as classic and contemporary stories, poems, folktales, songs, plays, and other genres.*

Analysis of Grade-Level-Appropriate Literary Text

1.3.1   Identify and describe the plot, setting, and character(s) in a story. Retell a story's beginning, middle, and ending.
Example: Read a story, such as *Arthur's Prize Reader* by Lillian Hoban. Retell the story, including descriptions of the characters and plot of the story, by telling about what happens to Arthur in the contest that he enters and the one that he helps his sister to enter. Plot the story onto a story map.

1.3.2   Describe the roles of authors and illustrators.
Example: Read a book, such as *The Very Hungry Caterpillar* by Eric Carle or *Where the Wild Things Are* by Maurice Sendak, in which the art is especially important in telling the story. Describe the role of the author and illustrator, and discuss how the pictures help to tell the story.

1.3.3   Confirm predictions about what will happen next in a story.
Example: Read part of a story, such as *The Musicians of Bremen: A Tale from Germany* by Jane Yolen or *Lilly's Purple Plastic Purse* by Kevin Henkes, and tell what might happen next and how the story might end.

1.3.4   Distinguish fantasy from reality.

1.3.5   Understand what is read by responding to questions (*who, what, when, where, why, how*).

WRITING: Processes and Features

Students discuss ideas for group stories and other writing. Students write clear sentences and paragraphs that develop a central idea. Students progress through the stages of the writing process, including prewriting, drafting, revising, and editing multiple drafts.

Organization and Focus

1.4.1   Discuss ideas and select a focus for group stories or other writing.

1.4.2   Use various organizational strategies to plan writing.

Evaluation and Revision

1.4.3   Revise writing for others to read.

Research Process and Technology

1.4.4   Begin asking questions to guide topic selection and ask *how* and *why* questions about a topic of interest.

1.4.5   Identify a variety of sources of information (books, online sources, pictures, charts, tables of contents, diagrams) and document the sources (titles)

1.4.6   Organize and classify information by constructing categories on the basis of observation.

WRITING: Applications (Different Types of Writing and Their Characteristics)

At Grade 1, students begin to write compositions that describe and explain familiar objects, events, and experiences. Students use their understanding of the sounds of words to write simple rhymes. Student writing demonstrates a command of Standard English and the drafting, research, and organizational strategies outlined in Standard 4 — Writing Processes and Features. Writing demonstrates an awareness of the audience (intended reader) and purpose for writing.

Using the writing strategies of Grade 1 outlined in Standard 4 — Writing Processes and Features, students:

1.5.1   Write brief narratives (stories) describing an experience.
Example: Write a short story titled *My Friend* describing an experience that is real or imagined.

1.5.2   Write brief expository (informational) descriptions of a real object, person, place, or event, using sensory details.
Example: Write a description of a family member, a pet, or a favorite toy. Include enough details so that the reader can picture the person, animal, or object.

1.5.3   Write simple rhymes.

1.5.4   Use descriptive words when writing.
Example: Use varied words to describe events, people, and places, such as describing a day as a *sunny day* or *cloudy day*.

1.5.5   Write for different purposes and to a specific audience or person.
Example: Write a thank-you note to the store manager after a field trip to the local supermarket.

WRITING: English Language Conventions

Students write using Standard English conventions appropriate to this grade level.

Handwriting

1.6.1   Print legibly and space letters, words, and sentences appropriately.

Sentence Structure

1.6.2   Write in complete sentences.

Grammar

1.6.3   Identify and correctly use singular and plural nouns (*dog/dogs*).

1.6.4   Identify and correctly write contractions (*isn't, aren't, can't*).

1.6.5   Identify and correctly write possessive nouns (*cat's meow, girls' dresses*) and possessive pronouns (*my/mine, his/hers*).

Punctuation

1.6.6   Correctly use periods (*I am five.*), exclamation points (*Help!*), and question marks (*How old are you?*) at the end of sentences.

Capitalization

1.6.7   Capitalize the first word of a sentence, names of people, and the pronoun *I*.

Spelling

1.6.8   Spell correctly three- and four-letter words (*can, will*) and grade-level-appropriate sight words (*red, fish*).

LISTENING AND SPEAKING: Skills, Strategies, and Applications

Students listen critically and respond appropriately to oral communication. They speak in a manner that guides the listener to understand important ideas by using proper phrasing, pitch, and modulation (raising and lowering voice). Students deliver brief oral presentations about familiar experiences or interests that are organized around a coherent thesis statement (a statement of topic). Students use the same Standard English conventions for oral speech that they use in their writing.

Comprehension

1.7.1   Listen attentively.

1.7.2   Ask questions for clarification and understanding.

1.7.3   Give, restate, and follow simple two-step directions.

Organization and Delivery of Oral Communication

1.7.4   Stay on the topic when speaking.

1.7.5   Use descriptive words when speaking about people, places, things, and events.

Speaking Applications

1.7.6   Recite poems, rhymes, songs, and stories.

1.7.7   Retell stories using basic story grammar and relating the sequence of story events by answering *who, what, when, where, why,* and *how* questions.

1.7.8   Relate an important life event or personal experience in a simple sequence.

1.7.9   Provide descriptions with careful attention to sensory detail.

1.7.10   Use visual aids, such as pictures and objects, to present oral information.

Looking Back: GRADE K

Indiana

English/Language Arts

Academic Standards

Grade **K**

Standard 1

READING: Word Recognition, Fluency, and Vocabulary Development

Students know about letters, words, and sounds. They apply this knowledge to read simple sentences.

Concepts About Print

K.1.1   Identify the front cover, back cover, and title page of a book.

K.1.2   Follow words from left to right and from top to bottom on the printed page.

K.1.3   Understand that printed materials provide information.

K.1.4   Recognize that sentences in print are made up of separate words.

K.1.5   Distinguish letters from words.

K.1.6   Recognize and name all capital and lowercase letters of the alphabet.

Phonemic Awareness*

K.1.7   Listen to two or three phonemes (sounds) when they are read aloud, and tell the number of sounds heard, whether they are the same or different, and the order. Example: Listen to the sounds /f/, /m/, /s/ or /l/, /n/, /v/. Tell how many sounds were heard and whether any sounds were the same.

K.1.8   Listen and say the changes in spoken syllables (a word or part of a word that contains one vowel sound) and words with two or three sounds when one sound is added, substituted, omitted, moved, or repeated. Example: Listen to the word *bat* and tell what word is left when you take the /b/ sound away. Tell what word is left when you take the /br/ sound away from the spoken word *brother*.

K.1.9 Listen to and say consonant-vowel-consonant (cvc) sounds and blend the sounds to make words.
Example: Listen to the sounds /b/, /e/, /d/ and tell what word is made.

K.1.10 Say rhyming words in response to an oral prompt.
Example: Say a word that rhymes with *cat*.

K.1.11 Listen to one-syllable words and tell the beginning or ending sounds.
Example: Tell what sound you hear at the beginning of the word *girl*.

K.1.12 Listen to spoken sentences and recognize individual words in the sentence; listen to words and recognize individual sounds in the words.

K.1.13 Count the number of syllables in words.

*When letters have a slanted line before and after them, such as /f/, /sh/, /b/, this represents the sound the letter makes, not the name of the letter.

Decoding and Word Recognition

K.1.14 Match all consonant sounds (<u>m</u>ad, <u>r</u>ed, <u>p</u>in, <u>t</u>op, <u>s</u>un) to appropriate letters.

K.1.15 Read one-syllable and high-frequency (often-heard) words by sight.

K.1.16 Use self-correcting strategies when reading simple sentences.

K.1.17 Read their own names.

K.1.18 Understand the alphabetic principle, which means that as letters in words change, so do the sounds.

K.1.19 Learn and apply knowledge of alphabetical order (first letter) when using a classroom or school library/media center.

Vocabulary and Concept Development

K.1.20 Identify and sort common words in basic categories.
Example: Tell whether the words *blue*, *yellow*, and *red* are colors, shapes, or foods. Tell the names of some favorite colors.

K.1.21 Identify common signs and symbols.
Example: Identify the meanings of common signs and symbols, such as stop signs or store signs, from the colors, shapes, logos, and letters on these signs or symbols.

K.1.22 Listen to stories read aloud and use the vocabulary in those stories in oral language.

Standard
2

READING: Comprehension and Analysis of Nonfiction and Informational Text

Students identify the basic facts and ideas in what they have read, heard, or seen. The selections in the **Indiana Reading List** *(www.doe.state.in.us/standards/ readinglist.html) illustrate the quality and complexity of the materials to be read by students. In Kindergarten, students will listen to and begin to read grade-level-appropriate nonfiction, such as alphabet books; picture books on science, social studies, mathematics and other subjects; and beginners' dictionaries.*

Structural Features of Informational and Technical Materials

K.2.1   Locate the title and the name of the author of a book.

Analysis of Grade-Level-Appropriate Nonfiction and Informational Text

K.2.2   Use pictures and context to aid comprehension and to draw conclusions or make predictions about story content.
Example: Tell how and where bees gather pollen after listening to a book about bees such as *The Honeymakers* by Gail Gibbons.

K.2.3   Generate and respond to questions (*who, what, where*).

K.2.4   Identify types of everyday print materials.
Example: Walk around the school and identify the signs in the school, such as EXIT, Principal's Office, and Restrooms. Tell the difference between a storybook and a beginners' dictionary.

K.2.5   Identify the order (first, last) of information.
Example: Listen to and look at the information in a book such as *Going on a Whale Watch* by Bruce McMillan. Then draw pictures representing the main events of a whale watching trip in the order in which they occurred.

READING: Comprehension and Analysis of Literary Text

Students listen and respond to stories based on well-known characters, themes, plots (what happens in a story), and settings (where a story takes place). The selections in the **Indiana Reading List** *(www.doe.state.in.us/standards/readinglist.html) illustrate the quality and complexity of the materials to be read by students. In Kindergarten, students will listen and respond to grade-level-appropriate fiction, such as classic and contemporary stories, Mother Goose nursery rhymes and other poems, songs, folktales, and plays.*

Analysis of Grade-Level-Appropriate Literary Text

K.3.1   Distinguish fantasy from reality.
Example: Listen to *The Day Jimmy's Boa Ate the Wash*, Trinka Hakes Noble's story about a class field trip to a farm, and *Farming*, Gail Gibbons' nonfiction book about farming. Tell how these two books are different.

K.3.2   Retell (beginning, middle, end) familiar stories.
Example: Retell the story of a folktale, such as the version of *The Three Little Pigs* by Steven Kellogg.

K.3.3   Identify characters, settings, and important events in a story.
Example: Identify the main characters in a story, such as *Noisy Nora* by Rosemary Wells. Describe the setting in a familiar story, such as *Goodnight Moon* by Margaret Wise Brown. Retell the important events in a story, such as the folktale *Jack and the Beanstalk*.

K.3.4   Identify favorite books and stories.

K.3.5   Understand what is heard or seen by responding to questions (*who, what, where*).

WRITING: Processes and Features

Students discuss ideas and tell stories for someone to write. Students use pictures, letters, and words to write.

Organization and Focus

K.4.1   Discuss ideas to include in a story.

K.4.2   Tell a story that the teacher or some other person will write.

K.4.3   Write using pictures, letters, and words.

K.4.4   Write phonetically spelled words (words that are written as they sound) and consonant-vowel-consonant words (demonstrating the alphabetic principle). Example: Write correctly simple words, such as *man, cat,* and *run,* and spell other words as they sound, such as *whale* as *wal, jumps* as *jmps,* and *bigger* as *bigr,* showing an understanding of what letters represent certain sounds.

K.4.5   Write by moving from left to right and from top to bottom.

Research Process and Technology

K.4.6   Ask *how* and *why* questions about a topic of interest.

K.4.7   Identify pictures and charts as sources of information and begin gathering information from a variety of sources (books, technology).

K.4.8   Organize and classify information into categories of how and why or by color or size.

WRITING: Applications (Different Types of Writing and Their Characteristics)

In Kindergarten, students begin to write and draw pictures for specific purposes and for a specific audience (intended reader).

K.5.1   Draw pictures and write words for a specific reason.
Example: Draw a picture or write to a friend or a family member to tell about something new at school.

K.5.2   Draw pictures and write for specific people or persons.
Example: Write or dictate an invitation to a parent to attend a classroom event.

WRITING: English Language Conventions

Students begin to learn the written conventions of Standard English.

Handwriting

K.6.1   Write capital and lowercase letters of the alphabet, correctly shaping and spacing the letters.

Spelling

K.6.2   Spell independently using an understanding of the sounds of the alphabet and knowledge of letter names.
Example: Spell correctly common words, such as *cat,* or spell by how the word sounds, such as *kat.*

LISTENING AND SPEAKING: Skills, Strategies, and Applications

Students listen and respond to oral communication. They speak in clear and coherent sentences. Students deliver brief oral presentations about familiar experiences or interests.

Comprehension

K.7.1   Understand and follow one- and two-step spoken directions.

Oral Communication

K.7.2   Share information and ideas, speaking in complete, coherent sentences.

Speaking Applications

K.7.3   Describe people, places, things (including their size, color, and shape), locations, and actions.

K.7.4   Recite short poems, rhymes, and songs.

K.7.5   Tell an experience or creative story in a logical sequence (chronological order, first, second, last).

Looking Ahead: GRADE 2

Indiana

English/Language Arts

Academic Standards

Grade 2

READING: Word Recognition, Fluency, and Vocabulary Development

Students understand the basic features of words. They see letter patterns and know how to translate them into spoken language by using phonics (an understanding of the different letters that make different sounds), syllables, and word parts (-s, -ed, -ing). They apply this knowledge to achieve fluent (smooth and clear) oral and silent reading.

Phonemic Awareness

2.1.1   Demonstrate an awareness of the sounds that are made by different letters by:
• distinguishing beginning, middle, and ending sounds in words.
• rhyming words.
• clearly pronouncing blends and vowel sounds.

Decoding and Word Recognition

2.1.2 Recognize and use knowledge of spelling patterns (such as *cut/cutting, slide/ sliding*) when reading.

2.1.3 Decode (sound out) regular words with more than one syllable (*dinosaur, vacation*).

2.1.4 Recognize common abbreviations (*Jan., Fri.*).

2.1.5 Identify and correctly use regular plural words (*mountain/mountains*) and irregular plural words (*child/children, mouse/mice*).

2.1.6 Read aloud fluently and accurately with appropriate changes in voice and expression.

2.1.11 Know and use common word families (such as *-ale, -est, -ine, -ock, -ump*) when reading unfamiliar words.

Vocabulary and Concept Development

2.1.7 Understand and explain common synonyms (words with the same meaning) and antonyms (words with opposite meanings).

2.1.8 Use knowledge of individual words to predict the meaning of unknown compound words (*lunchtime, lunchroom, daydream, raindrop*).

2.1.9 Know the meaning of simple prefixes (word parts added at the beginning of words such as *un-*) and suffixes (word parts added at the end of words such as *-ful*).

2.1.10 Identify simple multiple-meaning words (*change, duck*).

READING: Comprehension and Analysis of Nonfiction and Informational Text

Students read and understand grade-level-appropriate material. The selections in the **Indiana Reading List** *(www.doe.state.in.us/standards/readinglist.html) illustrate the quality and complexity of the materials to be read by students. At Grade 2, in addition to regular classroom reading, students read a variety of nonfiction, such as books in many different subject areas, children's magazines and periodicals, dictionaries, and other reference or technical materials).*

Structural Features of Informational and Technical Materials

2.2.1 Use titles, tables of contents, and chapter headings to locate information in text.

2.2.11 Identify text that uses sequence or other logical order (alphabetical order or time).

Analysis of Grade-Level-Appropriate Nonfiction and Informational Text

2.2.2 State the purpose for reading.
Example: Read an informational text about pets to decide what kind of animal would make the best pet.

2.2.3 Use knowledge of the author's purpose(s) to comprehend informational text.
Example: Read an informational text that compares different people, animals, or plants, such as *What Do You Do with a Tail Like This?* by Robin Page and Steve Jenkins.

2.2.4 Ask and respond to questions (*when, who, where, why, what if, how*) to aid comprehension about important elements of informational texts.
Example: After reading a short account about the first man on the moon, ask and answer *why, what if,* and *how* questions to understand the lunar landing.

2.2.5 Restate facts and details or summarize the main idea in the text to clarify and organize ideas.
Example: Summarize information learned from a text, such as detail about ant colonies stated in *Ant Cities* by Arthur Dorros or reported about spider webs in *Spider Magic* by Dorothy Hinshaw Patent.

2.2.6 Recognize cause-and-effect relationships in a text.
Example: Read an informational book that explains some common scientific causes and effects, such as the growth of a plant from a seed or the effects of different weather patterns, such as too much snow or rain at one time causing flooding.

2.2.7 Interpret information from diagrams, charts, and graphs.
Example: Use a five-day weather chart or a weather chart on the Internet to determine the weather for the coming weekend.

2.2.8 Follow two-step written instructions.

2.2.9 Use context (the meaning of the surrounding text) to understand word and sentence meanings.

2.2.10 Draw conclusions or confirm predictions about what will happen next in a text by identifying key words (signal words that alert the reader to a sequence of events, such as *before, first, during, while, as, at the same time, after, then, next, at last, finally, now, when* or cause and effect, such as *because, since, therefore, so*).

READING: Comprehension and Analysis of Literary Text

Students read and respond to a wide variety of significant works of children's literature. The selections in the **Indiana Reading List** *(www.doe.state.in.us/ standards/readinglist.html) illustrate the quality and complexity of the materials to be read by students. At Grade 2, students read a wide variety of fiction, such as classic and contemporary stories, poems, folktales, songs, plays, and other genres.*

Analysis of Grade-Level-Appropriate Literary Text

2.3.1 Compare plots, settings, and characters presented by different authors.
Example: Read and compare *Strega Nona*, an old Italian folktale retold by Tomie DePaola, with *Ox-Cart Man* by Donald Hall.

2.3.2 Create different endings to stories and identify the problem and the impact of the different ending.
Example: Read a story, such as *Fin M'Coul — The Giant of Knockmany Hill*, Tomie DePaola's retelling of an Irish folktale. Then, discuss different possible endings to the story, such as how the story would change if Fin's wife had not helped him or if Fin were not a giant.

2.3.3 Compare and contrast versions of same stories from different cultures.
Example: Compare fairy tales and folktales that have been retold by different cultures, such as *The Three Little Pigs* and the southwestern/Latino version *The Three Little Javelinas* by Susan Lowell, or *Cinderella* and the African version, *Mufaro's Beautiful Daughters* by John Steptoe.

2.3.4 Identify the use of rhythm, rhyme, and alliteration (using words with repeating consonant sounds) in poetry or fiction.
Example: Listen to or read the rhymes for each letter of the alphabet in *A My Name Is Alice* by Jane Bayer. Tell what effects the writer uses to make the poems fun to hear.

2.3.5 Confirm predictions about what will happen next in a story.

2.3.6 Recognize the difference between fantasy and reality.

2.3.7 Identify the meaning or lesson of a story.

WRITING: Processes and Features

Students write clear sentences and paragraphs that develop a central idea. Students progress through the stages of the writing process, including prewriting, drafting, revising, and editing multiple drafts.

Organization and Focus

2.4.1 Create a list of ideas for writing.

2.4.2 Organize related ideas together to maintain a consistent focus.

Research Process and Technology

2.4.3 Find ideas for writing stories and descriptions in pictures or books.

2.4.4 Understand the purposes of various reference materials (such as a dictionary, thesaurus, or atlas).

2.4.5 Use a computer to draft, revise, and publish writing.

Evaluation and Revision

2.4.6 Review, evaluate, and revise writing for meaning and clarity.

2.4.7 Proofread one's own writing, as well as that of others, using an editing checklist or list of rules.

2.4.8 Revise original drafts to improve sequence (the order of events) or to provide more descriptive detail.

WRITING: Applications (Different Types of Writing and Their Characteristics)

At Grade 2, students are introduced to letter writing. Students continue to write compositions that describe and explain familiar objects, events, and experiences. Students continue to write simple rhymes and poems. Student writing demonstrates a command of Standard English and the drafting, research, and organizational strategies outlined in Standard 4 — Writing Processes and Features. Writing demonstrates an awareness of the audience (intended reader) and purpose for writing.

In addition to producing the different writing forms introduced in earlier grades, Grade 2 students use the writing strategies outlined in Standard 4 — Writing Processes and Features to:

2.5.1   Write brief narratives based on experiences that:
• move through a logical sequence of events (chronological order, order of importance).
• describe the setting, characters, objects, and events in detail.
Example: Write a story about an experience that took place during a certain season in the year: spring, summer, fall, or winter. Tell the story in the order that it happened and describe it in enough detail so that the reader can picture clearly the place, people, and events.

2.5.2   Write a brief description of a familiar object, person, place, or event that:
• develops a main idea.
• uses details to support the main idea.
Example: Write a descriptive piece on a topic, such as *Houses Come in Different Shapes and Sizes.*

2.5.3   Write a friendly letter complete with the date, salutation (greeting, such as *Dear Mr. Smith*), body, closing, and signature.
Example: Write a letter to the police department in your town asking if someone can come to your classroom to talk about bicycle safety.

2.5.4   Write rhymes and simple poems.

2.5.5   Use descriptive words when writing.

2.5.6   Write for different purposes and to a specific audience or person.
Example: Write a description of your favorite book to recommend the book to a friend.

2.5.7   Write responses to literature that:
• demonstrate an understanding of what is read.
• support statements with evidence from the text.
Example: Write a description of a favorite character in a book. Include examples from the book to show why this character is such a favorite.

Research Application

2.5.8   Write or deliver a research report that has been developed using a systematic research process (defines the topic, gathers information, determines credibility, reports findings) and that:
• uses a variety of resources (books, technology, pictures, charts, tables of contents, diagrams) and documents sources (titles and authors).
• organizes information by categorizing it into single categories (such as size or color) or includes information gained through observation.
Example: After making observations and completing research at the library, write a report about animals that live in water or about different modes of transportation.

WRITING: English Language Conventions

Students write using Standard English conventions appropriate to this grade level.

Handwriting

2.6.1   Form letters correctly and space words and sentences properly so that writing can be read easily by another person.

Sentence Structure

2.6.2   Distinguish between complete (*When Tom hit the ball, he was proud.*) and incomplete sentences (*When Tom hit the ball*).

2.6.3   Use the correct word order in written sentences.

Grammar

2.6.4   Identify and correctly write various parts of speech, including nouns (words that name people, places, or things) and verbs (words that express action or help make a statement).
Example: Identify the noun and verb in a sentence, such as *Maria* (noun) *and a friend* (noun) *played* (verb) *for a long time.*

Punctuation

2.6.5   Use commas in the greeting (*Dear Sam,*) and closure of a letter (*Love,* or *Your friend,*) and with dates (*March 22, 2000*) and items in a series (*Tony, Steve, and Bill*).

2.6.6   Use quotation marks correctly to show that someone is speaking.
• Correct: "You may go home now," she said.
• Incorrect: "You may go home now she said."

Capitalization

2.6.7   Capitalize all proper nouns (names of specific people or things, such as *Mike, Indiana, Jeep*), words at the beginning of sentences and greetings, months and days of the week, and titles (*Dr., Mr., Mrs., Miss*) and initials in names.

Spelling

2.6.8   Spell correctly words like *was, were, says, said, who, what,* and *why,* which are used frequently but do not fit common spelling patterns.

2.6.9   Spell correctly words with short and long vowel sounds (*a, e, i, o, u*), r-controlled vowels (*ar, er, ir, or, ur*), and consonant-blend patterns (*bl, dr, st*).
• short vowels: actor, effort, ink, chop, unless
• long vowels: ace, equal, bind, hoe, use
• r-controlled: park, supper, bird, corn, further
• consonant blends: blue, crash, desk, speak, coast

LISTENING AND SPEAKING: Skills, Strategies, and Applications

Students listen critically and respond appropriately to oral communication. They speak in a manner that guides the listener to understand important ideas by using proper phrasing, pitch, and modulation (raising and lowering voice). Students deliver brief oral presentations about familiar experiences or interests that are organized around a point of view or thesis statement. Students use the same Standard English conventions for oral speech that they use in their writing.

Comprehension

2.7.1   Determine the purpose or purposes of listening (such as to obtain information, to solve problems, or to enjoy humor).

2.7.2   Ask for clarification and explanation of stories and ideas.

2.7.3   Paraphrase (restate in own words) information that has been shared orally by others.

2.7.4   Give and follow three- and four-step oral directions.

Organization and Delivery of Oral Communication

2.7.5   Organize presentations to maintain a clear focus.

2.7.6   Speak clearly and at an appropriate pace for the type of communication (such as an informal discussion or a report to class).

2.7.7   Tell experiences in a logical order (chronological order, order of importance, spatial order).

2.7.8   Retell stories, including characters, setting, and plot.

2.7.9   Report on a topic with supportive facts and details.

2.7.12   Use descriptive words when speaking about people, places, things, and events.

Speaking Applications

2.7.10   Recount experiences or present stories that:
• move through a logical sequence of events (chronological order, order of importance, spatial order).
• describe story elements, including characters, plot, and setting.

2.7.11   Report on a topic with facts and details, drawing from several sources of information.

2.7.13   Recite poems, rhymes, songs, and stories.

2.7.14   Provide descriptions with careful attention to sensory detail.